3

LONDON 1944

7

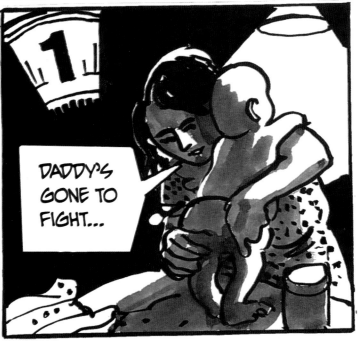

8

THIS WAS LONDON'S FIRST "DOODLEBUG" – THE V1 – HITLER'S 'VENGEANCE WEAPON' WITH ITS ONE TON WARHEAD. ITS AIMLESS TARGETING KILLED MRS ELLEN WOODCRAFT AND HER EIGHT-MONTH OLD BABY, TOM, TOGETHER WITH FOUR OTHER NEIGHBOURS ON GROVE ROAD IN BOW.

IT WAS TUESDAY 13 JUNE 1944. THE D-DAY INVASION WAS ONLY A WEEK EARLIER BUT NOW LONDONERS – WHO HAD THOUGHT THE WAR NEARLY OVER – PREPARED THEMSELVES FOR A SECOND BLITZ

I WOULDN'T LET HITLER MAKE ME CRY – NOT EVEN NOW 'E'S BROKE ME MUM'S BEST CHINA

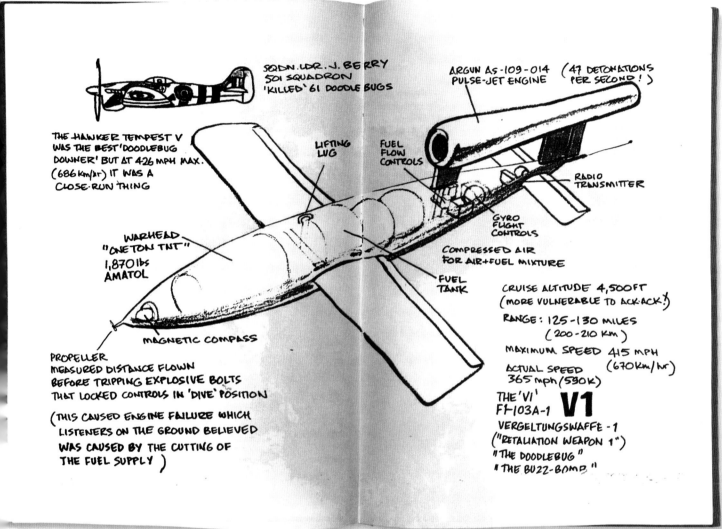

SQDN.LDR. J. BERRY
501 SQUADRON
'KILLED' 61 DOODLE BUGS

ARGUN AS-109-014
PULSE-JET ENGINE

(47 DETONATIONS
PER SECOND!)

THE HAWKER TEMPEST V
WAS THE BEST 'DOODLEBUG
DOWNER' BUT AT 426 MPH MAX.
(686 KM/hr) IT WAS A
CLOSE-RUN THING

LIFTING
LUG

FUEL
FLOW
CONTROLS

RADIO
TRANSMITTER

GYRO
FLIGHT
CONTROLS

WARHEAD
"ONE TON TNT"
1,870 lbs
AMATOL

COMPRESSED AIR
FOR AIR+FUEL MIXTURE

FUEL
TANK

CRUISE ALTITUDE 4,500 FT
(MORE VULNERABLE TO ACK-ACK!)

RANGE: 125-130 MILES
(200-210 KM)

MAGNETIC COMPASS

MAXIMUM SPEED 415 MPH
(670 KM/hr)

ACTUAL SPEED
365 mph (590 K)

PROPELLER
MEASURED DISTANCE FLOWN
BEFORE TRIPPING EXPLOSIVE BOLTS
THAT LOCKED CONTROLS IN 'DIVE' POSITION

THE 'VI'
FI-103A-1 **V1**

(THIS CAUSED ENGINE FAILURE WHICH
LISTENERS ON THE GROUND BELIEVED
WAS CAUSED BY THE CUTTING OF
THE FUEL SUPPLY)

VERGELTUNGSWAFFE - 1
("RETALIATION WEAPON 1")
"THE DOODLEBUG"
"THE BUZZ-BOMB "

WE WILL TURN LONDON INTO A GARDEN OF RUINS. PANIC WILL BREAK OUT IN ALL ENGLAND!

JUNE 1944

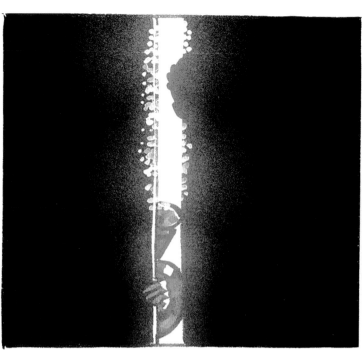

RAUS!

15

FROM PEENEMUNDE WHERE THEY DEVELOPED THIS 'SECRET WEAPON'

TO VAL YGOT WHERE THEY STILL REMEMBER IT

ARE YOU FROM THE RED CROSS?

NO, NO, I'M HERE SO YOU CAN TELL ME YOUR STORY...

THEN I'M GOING TO WRITE THE STORY OF YOU AND HITLER'S SECRET WEAPON:

THE "DOODLEBUG"

AH...THE V1!

PARIS 1941

FOUR YEARS BEFORE THE TRAGEDY OF GROVE ROAD, THE GERMAN ARMY HAD STEAMROLLERED OVER FRENCH RESISTANCE. A STUNNED NATION NOW HAD TO LEARN HOW TO LIVE UNDER NAZI RULE.

ICI LONDRES...

MICHEL! TURN IT DOWN!

SIT DOWN DEAR – DON'T MAKE WAVES...

YOU KNOW WE MUSN'T LISTEN TO THE BBC...

20

1918 20 YEARS OLD, MICHEL HOLLARD WATCHES THE DEFEATED GERMAN ARMY RETREAT

"I HAD JOINED THE ARMY AT SEVENTEEN YEARS OF AGE. IN 1918 WE THOUGHT WE HAD WON THE PEACE..."

BUT 1940 SAW THOSE DREAMS DESTROYED AS THE GERMAN ARMY RETURNED...

WE HAVE BEEN SAFE HERE IN GORNIES BUT NOW IT'S TIME...

TIME?

JULY 1940

IT'S TIME WE ALL GO BACK TO PARIS

1940 42 YEARS OLD, MICHEL HOLLARD WATCHES THE GERMAN ARMY MARCH THROUGH HIS PARIS

IT'S GOOD NEWS MICHEL, YOU CAN HAVE YOUR OLD JOB BACK – AND WITH A RAISE!

WORKING FOR THE NAZIS? – NO THANKS!

MY OLD COMPANY IS NOW WORKING FOR THE NAZIS – I MUST FIND A NEW JOB

STEAK? OH NO SIR, I'M SORRY – THE STEAKS ARE ONLY FOR THE WEHRMACHT

AND I HAD HOPED NEVER TO SEE THE GERMAN ARMY AGAIN...

DIJON

BACK AGAIN MONSIEUR HOLLARD?

SORTIE

WELCOME BACK, HOLLARD IT'S GOOD TO SEE YOU...

CAFÉ, HOLLARD?

IT SEEMS WE HAVE ANOTHER NEW CLIENT – THE GERMAN ARMY IS INTERESTED IN GAZOGÈNE

WE WANT YOU TO MEET THEM IN PARIS...

THIS IS A LIST OF THEIR CURRENT PRODUCTION OF MOTORS IN FRANCE – AND WHAT THEY WANT TO ORDER FROM US...

BUT DO WE WANT TO DO BUSINESS WITH THEM?

OH COME HOLLARD BUSINESS IS BUSINESS – EVEN MORE SO NOW

PARIS 1941

WHAT CAN I DO? WHAT **MUST** I DO?

I HAVE HERE ORDERS FOR YOUR MOTORS FROM THE KOMMANDATURA – THEY WILL NEED IMMEDIATE ATTENTION M'SIEUR HOLLARD...

THAT'S QUITE A LARGE ORDER...

JA! – BUT I'M SURE YOU WILL HANDLE IT WELL – WE ALL KNOW OUR DUTIES NOW DON'T WE?

HEIL HITLER!

GOOD DAY TO YOU...

31

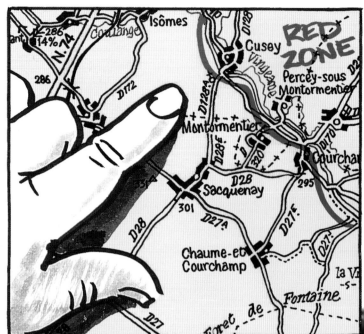

DE L'AUDACE, MICHEL, TOUJOURS DE L'AUDACE!

DAY TWO

YOU MUST COME TO THE FELDGENDARMERIE MONSIEUR HOLLARD

I DON'T LIKE THE LOOK OF THIS...

DAY THREE

38

I'M LOOKING FOR CHARCOAL WOOD FOR MY COMPANY...

I CAN GET MY MAN CUENOT TO SHOW YOU...

YOU CAN STAY CHEZ JACQOUT TONIGHT...

YOU FOUND JACQUOT AND CUENOT — AND I FOUND CHEZ ALAIN ET YVETTE

ET ENCORE UNE!

L'HOTEL BELLEVUE IN MONT-LE-BON

MICHEL HOLLARD HIKED THROUGH HERE LOOKING FOR A WAY TO AVOID THE GERMAN ARMY AND CROSS THE FRONTIER INTO SWITZERLAND. FOLLOWING HIS STEPS IN NOVEMBER, I WAS LUCKY ENOUGH TO FIND ALAIN & YVETTE WHO WERE SETTING UP THEIR HOTEL BELLEVUE FOR THE WINTER SKI SEASON AND COULD GIVE ME A BED.

DAY FOUR

THAT WAY'S FASTER...

BUT THIS WAY WE ARE LESS LIKELY TO MEET THE BOCHES

THAT'S GOOD!

ESPECIALLY AS I AM HOPING TO CROSS THE FRONTIER...

41

44

SNOW
COLD AUTUMN LEAVES
UNDER SWISS TREES
DAYGUS ELDERLY
... ON FREUNDEN

SWISS FRONTIER
AS MICHEL CROSSED IT
NINETY TIMES!

THAT'S TWENTY MILES TODAY

BERNE BERN

BERNE BERN

AND FOUR DAYS FROM DIJON...

MY SHOES ARE FALLING APART - AND MY FEET HURT!

BRITISH EMBASSY

MBASSADE OYAME UNI

AH! MON DIEU! CES ANGLAIS...

THEY PROBABLY THOUGHT THAT I WAS A NAZI 'PLANT'...

I LEFT THEM THAT WEHRMACHT MOTOR ORDER LIST – LET'S SEE IF THAT CONVINCES THEM. I'LL TRY AGAIN IN ONE MONTH...

MEANWHILE I'M A LONG WAY FROM HOME...

BUT NOW I KNOW THIS ROUTE CAN WORK

– SAFELY!

IN ENGLAND WE WERE FAR FROM 'SAFE' SLEEPING UNDER THE DINNER TABLE WHILE – UNKNOWN TO US KIDS – THERE WERE OTHER FRENCHMEN FIGHTING THE LUFTWAFFE ABOVE OUR HEADS...

'HENRY' LAFONT STOLE AN AEROPLANE TO JOIN THE RAF IN THE BATTLE OF BRITAIN – MANY YEARS LATER I WAS ABLE TO THANK HIM. IT WASN'T EASY TO DISOBEY MILITARY ORDERS – BUT: "I OBEY MY CONSCIENCE" HE SAID.

THEY FUELLED IT CAN BY JERRY CAN ALL NIGHT – THEN – IT NEARLY COULDN'T LIFT OFF AS THE PROPS WERE NOT SET RIGHT

THE GOELAND BI-MOTOR

GOELAND BI-MOTOR
There is a photo – using Henry's Leica – so broke in UK he sold it for £2.10s! 20 years old Sergeant-Pilot Henri Lafont steals a plane with René Marchotte et Guérin and flew to join the RAF 30 June 1940

19-03-03

Colonel 'Henry' Lafont

Prince Philip: Oh! So you pinched an aircraft

Last surviving Free French pilot of The Battle of Britain.

NOW, AS PROMISED, ONE MONTH AFTER HIS LAST DISAPPOINTING VISIT, MICHEL RETURNED TO BERNE. IT WAS 22 JUNE 1941...

– ANOTHER SUNDAY

BRITISH EMBASSY

...BASSADE ...ITANNIQUE

49

THE RETURN TO FRANCE:
CUENOT'S BARN DOOR CLOSED = DANGER!
BARN DOOR WIDE OPEN = SAFE TO CROSS

I WAS WORRIED ABOUT YOU –

YOUR SIGNAL WORKED THANK YOU

ONCE BACK IN FRANCE MICHEL HID HIS 'COUNTRY' CLOTHES

CÔTE DES HOMMES

– AND WOULD REAPPEAR AS THE BUSINESSMAN TO CATCH HIS TRAIN TO PARIS

MICHEL RISKED THIS DANGEROUS CROSSING 98 TIMES!

(DRAWINGS BY EMMANUEL GUIBERT)

54

87 years old and still frisky!

"BART"
JOSEPH BROCARD
GATTIERES 25 JAN 06

THE BRITISH ASKED US TO INVESTIGATE A NEW LUFTWAFFE BASE...

AÉRODROME DE CORMEILLES-EN-VEXIN

BART WAS DOING HIS USUAL GOOD WORK –

BUT THIS TIME, HE WAS CAUGHT RED-HANDED!

EVEN BART HAD NO EXCUSES THIS TIME

SO THEY THREW HIM INTO THEIR TEMPORARY JAIL IN HOUILLES TOWN HALL

ESCAPE LOOKED IMPOSSIBLE...

41CMS BY 51 CMS – BUT THE FRAME IS WOOD!

BART FINALLY FORCED THE WINDOW 'OPEN'

USING THE SOUND OF A PASSING TRAIN TO HIDE THE NOISE - AND TAKING HIS BLANKET AS A HOPEFUL PARACHITE

-HE JUMPED!

HE HAD FALLEN INTO A GARDEN - BUT IT WAS A THIRD FLOOR JUMP AND LYING THERE IN AGONY HE KNEW HE WAS HURT - BADLY...

HERE, GIVE ME YOUR PEN AND I'LL SHOW YOU...

(DRAWING BY BART OF HIS CRUSHED VERTIBRAE AFTER ESCAPING VIA THE THREE FLOOR JUMP)

WOULD THE HOUSE HELP HIM - OR TURN HIM BACK TO PRISON?

HÔTEL DE LA GARE DE LYON GRILL ROOM

MICHEL'S REGULAR BASE FOR AGENTS IN PARIS

BART! WHAT ARE YOU DOING HERE?

DID THEY LET YOU OUT TO SPY ON US — OR DID YOU REALLY ESCAPE?

MICHEL! I BROKE MY BACK!

BUT DID YOU TELL THEM ANYTHING?

NOTHING, MICHEL. I SWEAR IT — NOTHING!

YOU KNOW HE MUST NOT BE MOVED...

OR COURSE, DOCTOR, OF COURSE...

61

NOT EVERYONE WAS WILLING OR ABLE TO HELP...

NO! NO!

DO NOT PRESUME TO TELL ME MY DUTY...

I HAVE A FAMILY M'SIEUR, MY DUTY IS TO THEM...

NO — I CANNOT HELP YOU... I HAVE TO BE CAREFUL... WE SHOULD ALL BE CAREFUL...

NOW GO! — GO! BEFORE I CALL THE POLICE...

I'VE WORKED ON THIS LINE FOR TWELVE YEARS AND IT HURTS WHEN I SEE ALL THAT DAMAGE TO MY LINE...

SERVICE D'AUTOBUS REMPLAÇANT →

- BUT IT DOES REALLY UPSET THE "MASTER RACE"

WE CERTAINLY AGREE THERE! - MAY I ASK YOUR NAME?

WHY? ARE YOU POLICE?

NO! - I'M NOT ONE OF THEM, I JUST THOUGHT YOU MIGHT BE ABLE TO HELP ME 'UPSET' THE "MASTER RACE" - MY NAME'S HOLLARD, MICHEL HOLLARD

RAUZIER...

"SOME SAID 'NO' – SOME SAID 'YES' – BUT I ENDED UP WITH GOOD AGENTS COVERING ALL THE MAIN RAIL JUNCTIONS. DID I TELL YOU ABOUT RAUZIER? HE WAS THE RAIL DISPATCH CLERK AT NIMES..."

NIMES

OH! OH! LES BOCHES SONT ICI

WHAT THE HELL ARE THEY AFTER?

NIMES

66

MY CHILDREN...

YOUR MOTHER AND I HAVE DECIDED THAT WE MUST MOVE TO A SAFER PLACE...

WE MUST ALL "DISAPPEAR" — JUST FOR A WHILE...

D 906
St REMY-LES CHEVREUSE

KIDS ARE WONDERFUL AREN'T THEY? THEY NEVER COMPLAINED ALL THROUGH THOSE TOUGH TIMES

OH! WE COMPLAINED — BUT WE STILL HAD TO GO — LONDON WAS A TARGET AGAIN

Café Aux Chasseurs

IT LOOKS LIKE THE WEHRMACHT WANT TO SHOW ME THE WAY...

I WAS CHECKING 5KS IN EACH DIRECTION – AND 5KS UP THAT ROAD I FOUND IT.

FOUND WHAT?

I COULDN'T KNOW THEN – SO I HAD TO HAVE A CLOSER LOOK

WHAT ABOUT THE GUARDS?

THE SITE WAS GUARDED, YES... – BUT AGAINST WHAT?

I DIDN'T THINK THEY WOULD STOP A WORKER

SO I CAME OUT OF THE BUSHES PULLING UP MY PANTS AS IF I HAD TAKEN A TOILET BREAK...

AND WENT "BACK TO WORK" WITH "MY" BORROWED WHEELBARROW

THEY WERE CHECKING PASSES AT THE GATE...

I HOPED MY WHEELBARROW WAS MY PASS...

73

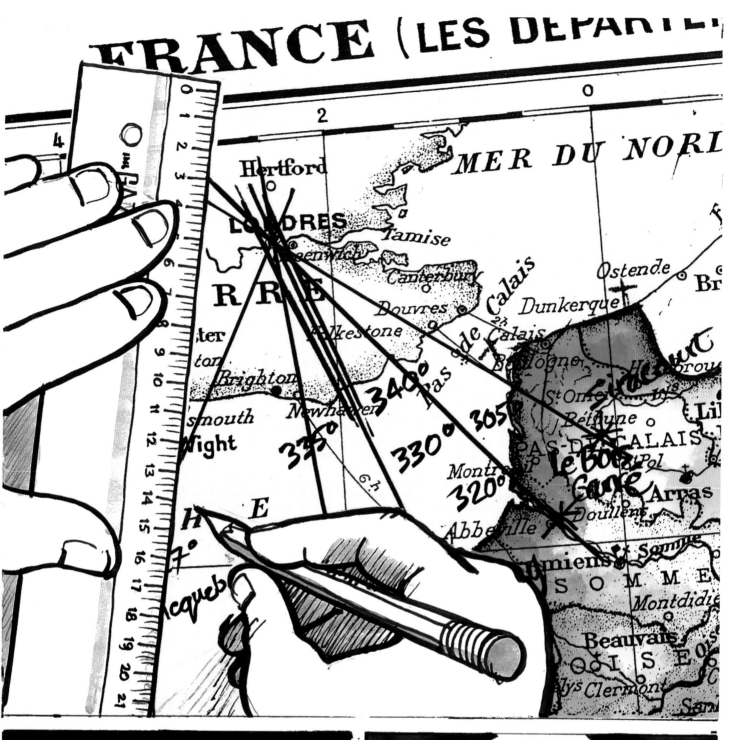

DIRECTION LONDRES!

ROBERT TAKES PHOTOS...

FRANÇOIS DE LACROIX — COMME l'AUTEUR!

FERME DE LA CROIX
LE BONNETOT LE FAUBOURG

LAWRENCE

M. L'ABBEY DUFOR

ROBERT de BOSMELET

ANTHONY HUGHES

MEMOIRE OF ARNHEM — REGIMENTAL TIE "THE BLUES"

YOU HAVE A LOT OF FRIENDS IN AUFFAY — THEY HELPED ME A LOT

THEY TOOK ME TO THAT FIRST SITE THAT YOU FOUND ON DELACROIX FARM — THERE IS STILL THAT GAP IN THE TREES POINTING TO LONDON...

75

WE NEEDED TO KNOW MORE...
I WAS ABLE TO SET UP A TEAM OF
NEW VOLUNTEERS AND EQUIP
THEM WITH BICYCLES TO COMB
THE CHANNEL AREA LOOKING FOR
MORE SITES LIKE THE
DELACROIX FARM

BY THE END OF NOVEMBER
WE HAD FOUND SIXTY SITES...

AND BY OCTOBER - A HUNDRED!

WE KNEW **WHERE** THEY WERE
BUT WE STILL DIDN'T KNOW
WHAT THEY WERE **FOR**...

AND THEN I HAD
AN AMAZING BIT
OF GOOD LUCK -
I MET ANDRE COMPS

WHAT DO YOU DO EXACTLY
AT 'BOIS CARRE'
MONSIEUR COMPS?

I'M AN
ARCHITECTURAL
DRAUGHTSMAN...

YOU MIGHT BE THE ONE MAN
IN ALL OF FRANCE WHO CAN GET
US EXACT PLANS OF THESE SITES

IT WOULD BE
DANGEROUS - BUT I WILL TRY...

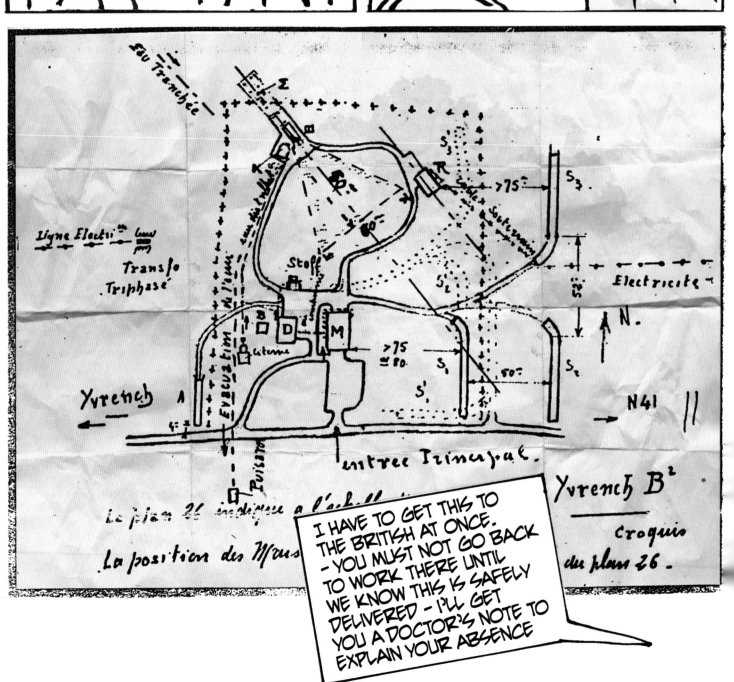

I HID THE MAP IN PLAIN SIGHT WITH MY GAZOGÈNE TECH. DRAWINGS..

BUT I KNEW THAT WOULDN'T WORK IF THE GUARDS SEARCHED ME ON THE SWISS FRONTIER...

IF I WAS CAUGHT WITH THE MAP — IT WAS SO OBVIOUSLY ANDRE'S WORK, IT WOULD HAVE BEEN A BULLET FOR BOTH OR US...

(45 YEAR OLD MICHEL HOLLARD — FIT AS A FIDDLE!)

— SO I RETRACED MICHEL'S PATH TO UNDERSTAND THE RISKS HE TOOK CROSSING THE GUARDED FRONTIER 98 TIMES

(OLD JED FALBY OUT-OF-BREATH ON SWISS FRONTIER)

IT WAS HIS INFORMATION THAT ALLOWED THE RAF TO FIND THESE CAMOUFLAGED SITES...

(YOUNG JED FALBY SERVING IN RAF)

TWO F24 FORWARD FACING
OBLIQUES SYNCHRONISED
FOR STEREO VIEWING

WITH ONLY
VERTICAL PHOTOS
THEY THOUGHT
THE V2'S WERE
"SILOS"

IF YOU HAD NEVER
SEEN A ROCKET
THAT'S A GOOD
GUESS

F52 FORWARD FACING
OBLIQUE

SPLIT F24   OR 1 K17

SPLIT
F52
F24

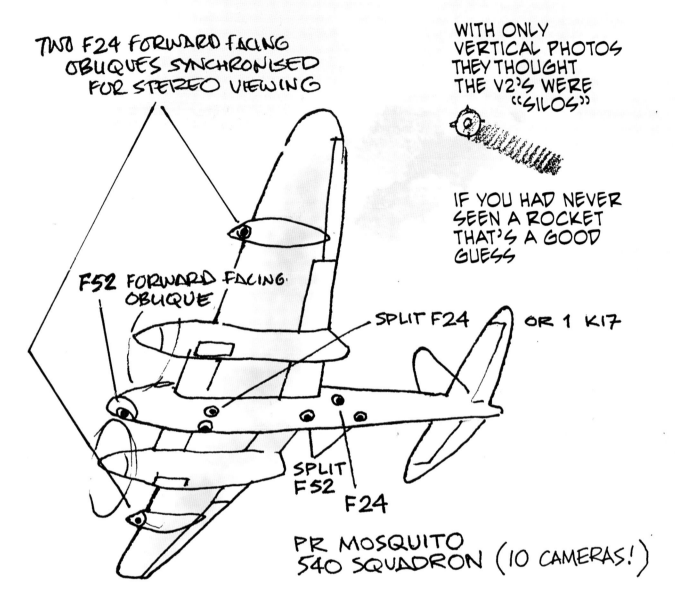

PR MOSQUITO
540 SQUADRON (10 CAMERAS!)

GUIDED BY ANDRE'S MAP AND MICHEL'S GROUNDWORK WITH
HIS 'AGIR' TEAM, THE RAF PHOTO RECONNAISSANCE MOSQUITOS
CAME LOOKING FOR
THESE STRANGE NEW
WEAPON SITES...

BY DECEMBER 1943
MICHEL AND THE
RAF HAD INDENTIFIED
75 SITES IN THE
PAS-DE-CALAIS

YES, MICHEL,
-BUT WHEN WILL
THE BOMBERS
COME?

FOUND IT!
'LE BOIS CARRÉ
(YVRENCH)

- A VERY ORDINARY LOOKING SMALL FRENCH WOOD
- NO MARKERS
- NO MEMORIALS
- AND THE LOCALS DON'T KNOW - OR HAVE CHOSEN TO FORGET - ITS HISTORY

IT WAS CHRISTMAS DAY 1943 WHEN THE RAF FINALLY ARRIVED - ANDRE WAS HOME FOR THE HOLIDAYS AND SO ESCAPED THE BOMBS

THE GERMANS ORDERED HIM BACK ON-SITE TO REPAIR THE DAMAGE!

IT'S STILL A DANGEROUS PLACE TO WALK IN - THE CRATERS ARE BIG ENOUGH TO SWALLOW A BUS!

WE HAD LOCATED MANY OF THESE V1 SITES AMD PASSED THE DETAILS TO THE BRITISH. IT WAS FRUSTRATING, AFTER ALL THAT RISKY WORK WE STILL DID NOT KNOW WHAT SORT OF WEAPON THESE RAMPS WERE FOR

BUT THEN I GOT A MESSAGE FROM PIERRE BOURDON – THE STATION MASTER – AT AUFFAY...

BONG!

STRANGE THINGS ARE HAPPENING HERE. WALK WITH ME TO THE STATION

LOOK OVER MY SHOULDER AS WE WALK...

WHATEVER IT IS THEY CERTAINLY DON'T WANT ANYBODY LOOKING AT IT

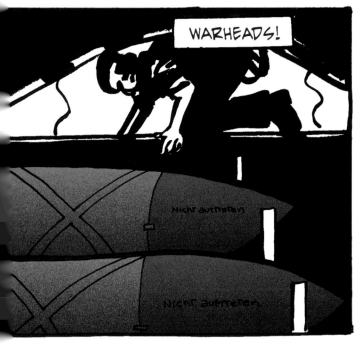

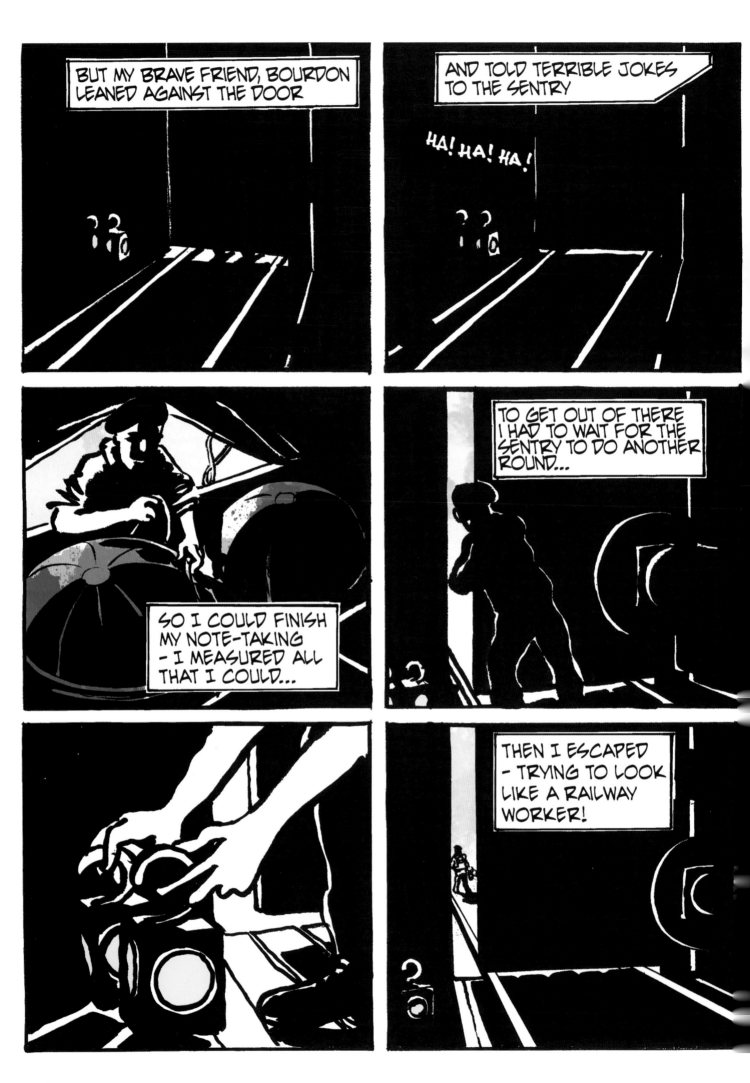

84

HAVE THEY SEEN US?

NO – IF THEY HAD SEEN US THEY WOULD BE SHOOTING!

WINTER WAS DIFFICULT...

I HAD TO COME UP WITH A WAY TO LEAVE NO TRACKS IN THE SNOW FOR THE GUARDS TO SEE

NOW WE KNOW WHAT THE WEAPONS ARE AND WE KNOW WHERE THEY ARE...WHAT NEXT?

WAIT AND SEE I'M AFRAID...

ROBERT AND FRANÇOIS DELACROIX (LIKE THE ARTIST!)

AND THE OLD FIRING CONTROL POST ON THE DELACROIX FARM (BONNETOT)

IN JANUARY THE RAF HIT MICHEL'S FIRST SITE – HERE AT BONNETOT. THE HALIFAX BOMBERS HIT THE FARM AND KILLED LOTS OF COWS – BUT NOT ONE BOMB HIT THE V1 SITE THEY WERE FAR TOO HIGH

18,000 FT – AND AT NIGHT!

WHICH IS WHY THE RAF SWITCHED TO MOSQUITOS – FIGHTER-BOMBERS THAT – AT GREAT RISK – ATTACKED AT LOW LEVEL WITH MUCH MORE ACCURACY.

THE RAF LOVED OUR CHATEAU. – IN FACT THEY CAME BACK TO VISIT SEVEN TIMES...

ROBERT DE BOSMELET
18 NOV 2006

86

CHATEAU DE BOSMELET
FEB. 1944

IF YOU EVER MEET AN OLD MOSQUITO PILOT YOU SHAKE HIS HAND FOR ME

'BART'A 87 ans
JOSEPH BROCARD
GATTIERES 25 JAN 07

blöde.. stechmücke! *

* DAMN MOSQUITOS!

BONNETOT

HERBOUVILLE

FREVAL

IT IS WITH REGRET, SIR, THAT I MUST REPORT THAT OUR LAUNCH DATE WILL HAVE TO BE REVISED...

BOSMELET

THE LAUNCH SITE OUT BEHIND THE STABLES NEVER FIRED A SINGLE V1 — THE RAF JUST NEVER LET THEM FINISH IT. — A GOOD REWARD FOR ALL MICHEL'S WORK...

SO ALL YOUR WORK HAD PAID OFF... WHY DIDN'T YOU STOP?

HOW COULD WE STOP? THE GERMANS WERE STILL WITH US. — AND THE ALLIES A LONG WAY OFF

CAFÉ AUX CHASSEURS
176 FAUBOURG ST. DENIS
5 FEBRUARY 1944
(LEGENDRE, DUJARIER, MAILLY, WAIT FOR MICHEL)

(60 YEARS ON)
NOV 2004

SALUT MICHEL!
– CAFÉ?

MONSIEUR HOLLARD!

MICHEL?

NO!

91

SO THEY FINALLY HAD YOU...

BUT THEY DIDN'T HAVE MY TEAM – AND MY ONE LAST DUTY WAS TO PROTECT THEM

HOW COULD YOU PROTECT THEM?

ONLY ONE WAY – BY NOT GIVING IN TO THE GESTAPO TORTURE...

WE'RE WASTING OUR TIME WITH THIS PIG-HEADED FOOL...

THANK GOD THEY TIRED OF THE BUSINESS BEFORE I DID....

TORTURE IS LIKE A TERRIBLE TOOTHACHE – ONCE PASSED YOU CAN FORGET IT – BUT WAITING FOR IT – THE DREADFUL ANTICIPATION...

– THAT'S THE NIGHTMARE THAT CAN BREAK THE STRONGEST OF MEN

BUT YOU DIDN'T BREAK...

BUT MORE IMPORTANT LEGENDRE – ARRESTED WITH ME – WAS RELEASED IN TIME FOR D-DAY...

THIS IS THE BBC HOME SERVICE... HERE IS A SPECIAL BULLETIN READ BY JOHN SNAGGE...

LONDON 6 JUNE 1944

EARLY TODAY ALLIED FORCES UNDER THE COMMAND OF GENERAL EISENHOWER MADE SEVERAL LANDINGS ON THE FRENCH COAST

D-DAY WAS INCREDIBLE IN LONDON - YOU WOULD HAVE THOUGHT THE WAR WAS OVER...

DAD TOOK DOWN THE BLACK OUT CURTAINS

WE CAN PAINT THE KITCHEN NOW - THAT WILL PLEASE YOUR MUM...

THE GAS MASKS WERE FORGOTTEN IN THE HALL...

NO MORE SLEEPING IN THE SHELTER NOW - IT'LL SOON ALL BE OVER!

AT NIGHT WE ALL SLEPT IN OUR MORRISON SHELTER

DURING THE DAY IT WAS OUR DINING TABLE

WALKING TO SCHOOL WE PASSED LINES OF TANKS ON THEIR WAY TO NORMANDY

DAD WAS STILL ON FIREWATCH BUT THE RAIDS HAD GONE QUIET FOR SOME MONTHS NOW...

DOUG! LISTEN! WHAT'S THAT NOISE?

DIVER! DIVER!*

* THE OFFICIAL CODE NAME FOR THE FLYING BOMB

-BUT THEN THE STORM BROKE AND HITLER LAUNCHED HIS FIRST WAVE OF 244 V1 FLYING BOMBS AT LONDON 244 IN JUST ONE DAY!

OH GOD! A DOODLEBUG!

LONDON 17TH JUNE 1944 10:32 HRS:

WHEN I HEARD THAT I THOUGHT ALL OUR WORK, ALL THOSE RISKS, HAD BEEN FOR NOTHING -

BUT NO! - MICHEL, HITLER LAUNCHED 244 BOMBS THAT FIRST DAY - BUT ONLY 73 GOT TO HIT LONDON

LONDON, Saturday 17th June 1944 **10:00 am**

AT HOME - A NEAR MISS BLEW OUR FRONT DOOR IN

ARE YOU OK HERE? - THEY HIT THE 'PRINCE ALBERT'

OH DEAR THOSE POOR MEN...

WHAT MEN LUV?

WHY - THE CREW ON THE 'PRINCE ALBERT'

IT'S NOT A SHIP, LUV, IT'S THE PUB

AND LUCKILY IT WASN'T EVEN OPENING TIME!

THAT DOES IT! WE HAVE TO GET THE CHILDREN AWAY

AGAIN?

SO WE WERE EVACUATED AGAIN, FOR THE FOURTH TIME!

- THEY WERE CHASED BY THE R.A.F. CAPITAINE JEAN MIRADOR FLYING IN HIS SPITFIRE MKXIV HAD ALREADY 'KILLED' 9 V1S AND WAS AFTER MORE...

HE WAS GOING TO MARRY 'WAAF' JEAN LAMBOUM ON THE 10TH AUG.1944...

BUT, ON THE 3RD AUGUST 1944 HIS TENTH DOODLEBUG BLEW UP IN MID-AIR AND TOOK HIM DOWN WITH IT

THERE WERE GUNS...

65!

AUGUST 28 1944 AA GUNS SCORE: 65 V1s

THERE WERE PLANES...

23!

AUGUST 28 1944 RAF SCORE: 23 V1s

BUT THE KEY BATTLE HAD BEEN WON BEFORE WHEN YOU IDENTIFIED THE THREAT AND SPOTLIGHTED THE SITES

AUGUST 28 1944 V1 HITS ON LONDON: 4

IT MUST BE SO FRUSTRATING FOR YOU HERE

IT'S IMPORTANT NOT TO GIVE IN TO DESPAIR... I ORGANISE TALKS — TRY TO HELP THE SICK...

TEN MONTHS AT NEUENGAMME SEEMS LIKE TEN YEARS — AND WITH THE ALLIES APPROACHING I'M SURE THE GERMANS WILL NOT LET US LIVE...

GIVE ME YOUR HANDS —
LET US MAKE A CHAIN TOGETHER
AND I WILL PRAY FOR GOD'S HELP
ON BEHALF OF US ALL...

WE HAD NO WAY OF KNOWING HOW LONG WE WERE PENNED IN THERE...EIGHT? NINE? DAYS...

THAT'S ALL THE LIFEBOATS DESTROYED, SIR...

JUST KEEP THE CAPTAIN'S CUTTER FOR YOUR TEAM WHEN WE DROWN THESE RATS

SHHHHH! LISTEN!

BOOM! BOOM!

WE COULD HEAR THE ALLIES GETTING CLOSER – BUT IT SEEMED THE NAZIS HADN'T FINISHED WITH US YET...

ALL FRENCH PRISONS ON DECK – NOW! –

THEY SAY HITLER'S DEAD!

DEAD? HITLER'S DEAD!

DEAD?

HITLER DEAD? – AND ME STILL LIVING? HOW CAN THAT BE?

110

BEFORE MICHEL COULD FINALLY FLY HOME TO A HERO'S WELCOME.

THE SKIES OVER LONDON WERE SAFE AGAIN – AND ALL THE PLANES WE COULD SEE WERE FRIENDLY

YOU COULD TELL THAT STORY IN A BOOK, GRANDAD...

MAYBE I WILL... MAYBE I WILL...